Commissioned by Hilary Hahn as part of the Encores project, 2010

First performed on 13 October 2011 in Memorial Hall, Cincinnati
by Hilary Hahn (violin) and Valentina Lisitsa (piano)

for Hilary Hahn

WHISPERING

EINOJUHANI RAUTAVAARA
(b 1928)

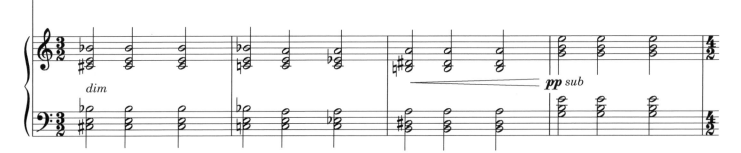

19164

Einojuhani
Rautavaara

Whispering

Violin & piano

Boosey & Hawkes Music Publishers Ltd
www.boosey.com

Published by Boosey & Hawkes Music Publishers Ltd
Aldwych House
71–91 Aldwych
London
WC2B 4HN

www.boosey.com

ISMN 979-0-060-12612-3
ISBN 978-0-85162-849-3

This impression 2014

Printed by Halstan:
Halstan UK, 2–10 Plantation Road, Amersham, Bucks, HP6 6HJ. United Kingdom
Halstan DE, Weißliliengasse 4, 55116 Mainz. Germany

Music origination by The Note Factory

Einojuhani

Rautavaara

Whispering
for violin & piano

Violin part

Boosey & Hawkes Music Publishers Ltd
www.boosey.com

for Hilary Hahn

WHISPERING

Violin

EINOJUHANI RAUTAVAARA
(b 1928)

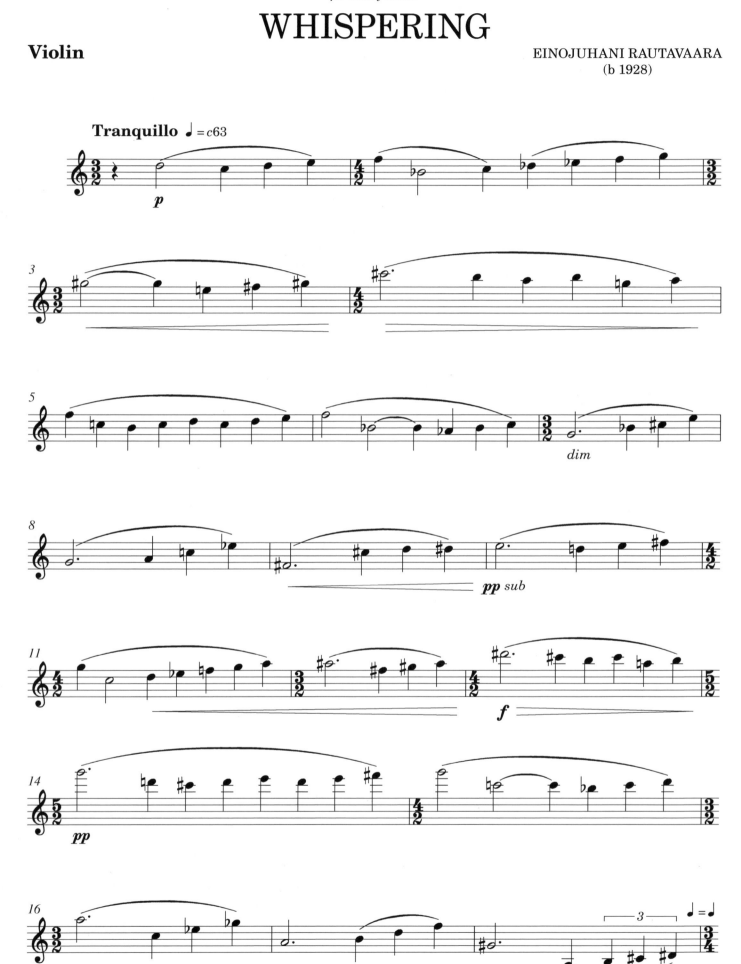

19164

Con brio

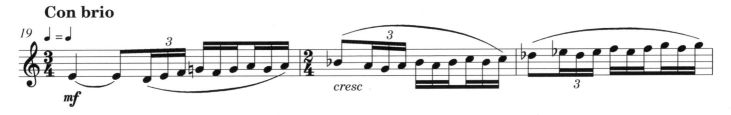

Tranquillo

Published by Boosey & Hawkes Music Publishers Ltd
Aldwych House
71–91 Aldwych
London
WC2B 4HN

www.boosey.com

© Copyright 2010 by Boosey & Hawkes Music Publishers Ltd

ISMN 979-0-060-12612-3
ISBN 978-0-85162-849-3

This impression 2014

Printed by Halstan:
Halstan UK, 2–10 Plantation Road, Amersham, Bucks, HP6 6HJ. United Kingdom
Halstan DE, Weißliliengasse 4, 55116 Mainz. Germany

Music origination by The Note Factory

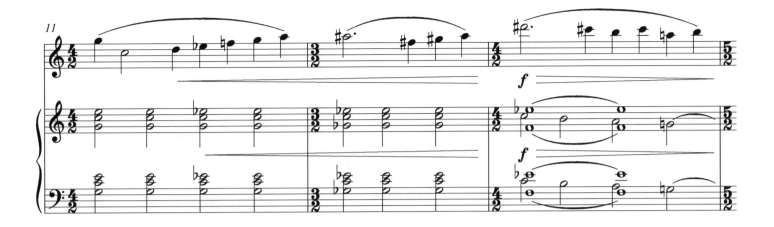

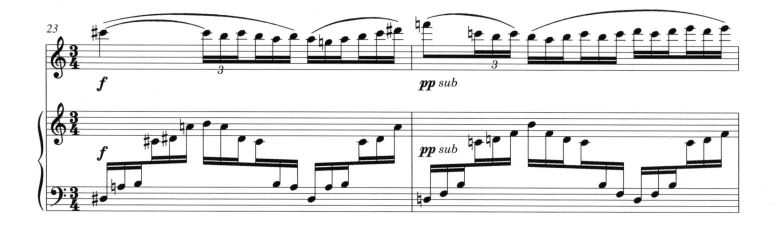

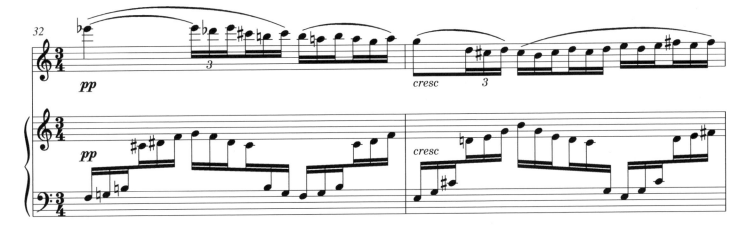

Tranquillo

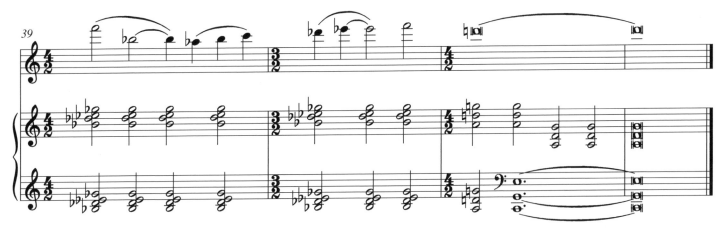

BOOSEY & HAWKES
CONCERT REPERTOIRE FOR VIOLIN & PIANO

Bartók	First Rhapsody
	Second Rhapsody
Bernstein	Sonata
Blacher	Sonata
Bridge	Souvenir
Britten	Three Pieces from Suite op 6
Copland	Duo
	Hoe-Down from Rodeo
	Nocturne
	Sonata
	Suite from Appalachian Spring
Delius	Sonatas 1, 2 & 3
	Sonata in B (posthumous)
Dohnányi	Sonata in C sharp minor op 21
Elgar	Offertoire
Ferguson	Sonatas 1 & 2
Fine	Sonata
Finzi	Elegy
	Introit
Gál	Sonata in B flat minor op 17
	Sonata in D (1933)
	Suite
Ginastera	Pampeana no 1 (Rhapsody)
Goldschmidt	Encore, une méditation agitée …
	Rondeau 'Rue du Rocher'
Howells	Sonata in B minor (1911)
	Sonata no 1 op 18 (1918)
Ireland	Sonata in A minor
Jolivet	Suite rhapsodique
Laks	Suite polonaise
Medtner	Sonata no 1 in B minor
	Three Nocturnes
Prokofieff	Five Melodies op 35b
	Sonata no 1 op 80
Rachmaninoff	Morceaux de salon
Schreker	Sonata in F major
Stanford	Irish Rhapsody no 6
Stravinsky	Chanson Russe
	Divertimento
	Duo Concertant
	Suite Italienne
Thomson	Sonata no 1

Ad 488